£2.45

Printed and Published in Great Britain by D. C. THOMSON & CO., LTD.,

185 Fleet Street, London EC4A 2HS.   © D. C. THOMSON & CO., LTD., 1985.
ISBN 0 85116 324 6

"BEANO" BABES

THE EDITOR HAS BORROWED SOME OF THE VERY FIRST PHOTOS OF YOUR "BEANO" PALS FROM THEIR FAMILY ALBUMS....

MINNIE the MINX

Tail wail!

The BASH STREET KIDS

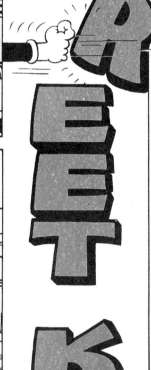

SIGH! I'M BORED.

ERK! I'VE TWIDDLED MY THUMBS SO MUCH LOOK WHAT'S HAPPENED!

TWIDDLE

STUCK

SMUDGE

NNF! THAT DOES IT— I'M GOING TO FIND SOMETHING EXCITING TO DO!

PLOP!

So—

I'VE DECIDED TO TAKE UP POT-HOLING.

A savage beast? Not in the least!

TOM, DICK and SALLY

What A Potty Player!

"BEANO" BABES

BILLY

WHIZZ

Everyone's going to be throwing!

Whee——crunch! What a punch!

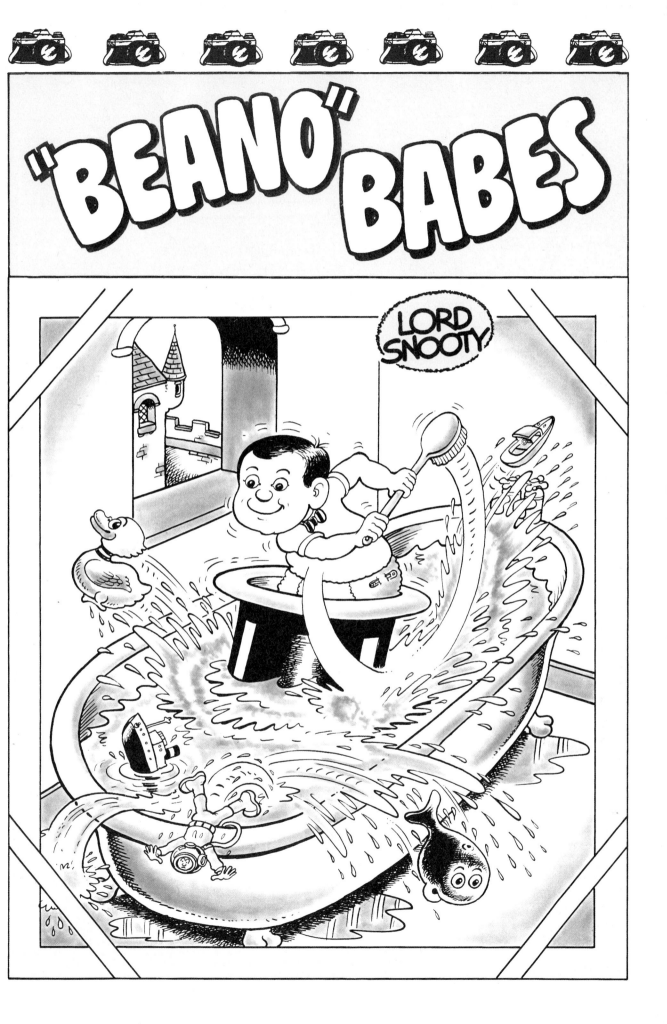

Pushed out without a doubt!

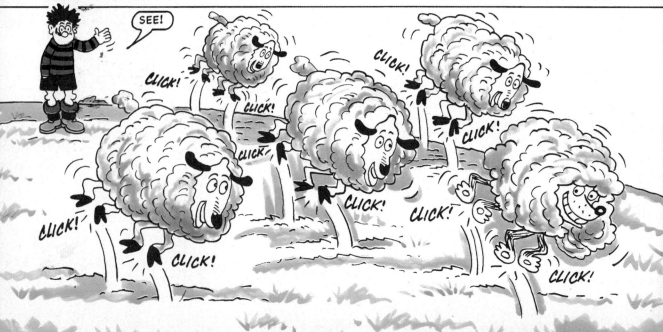

Judges agog—no dog!

A quick trip into a sheep dip!

FUN ON THE CARDS

HUH! IT'S RAINING AGAIN.

I KNOW—WE CAN PLAY CARDS.

WOULD YOU LIKE A QUIET GAME OF CARDS, WALTER?

OOH! LOVELY— I'LL BE RIGHT OVER, DENNIS!

Bye-bye, rented sty!

Arcade raid!

Olive's food does some good!

A silly goon with a balloon!

"BEANO" BABES

A shock to come for our grubby chum!

ROGER the DODGER

Too bad—a wobbly Dad!

String thing!

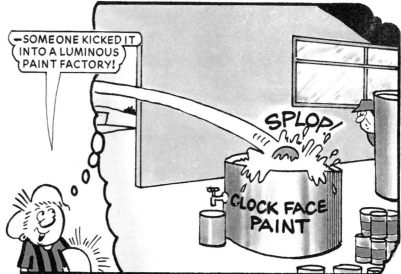

LITTLE PLUM

"BEANO" BABES

LITTLE PLUM

Rock shock!

"BEANO" BABES

THE LIBRARY –

VERY POPULAR. MAIN FEATURE A COMPLETE COLLECTION OF "BEANO" BOOKS AND "BEANO" COMICS!

CANNONS –

DON'T GO TOO NEAR THEM – YOU MIGHT GET SOAKED IF MY PALS DECIDE TO HAVE A WATER-CANNON FIGHT!

SECRET PASSAGE –

USE THE SECRET PASSAGE TO COLLECT A SUPER SOUVENIR OF YOUR VISIT – SOME OF AUNT MAT'S JAM TARTS!

GRAND STAIRCASE –

IDEAL PRACTICE FOR YOUR WINTER SKI-ING HOLIDAY!

PICTURE GALLERY—

THE ARMOURY—
HIDE IN ONE OF OUR SUITS OF ARMOUR IF THE GASWORKS GANG ATTACK!

AND REMEMBER—
DO TAKE ONE OF THE OLD GUIDE BOOKS WITH YOU! THEY'RE MOST HANDY!

Animals should have suitable food!

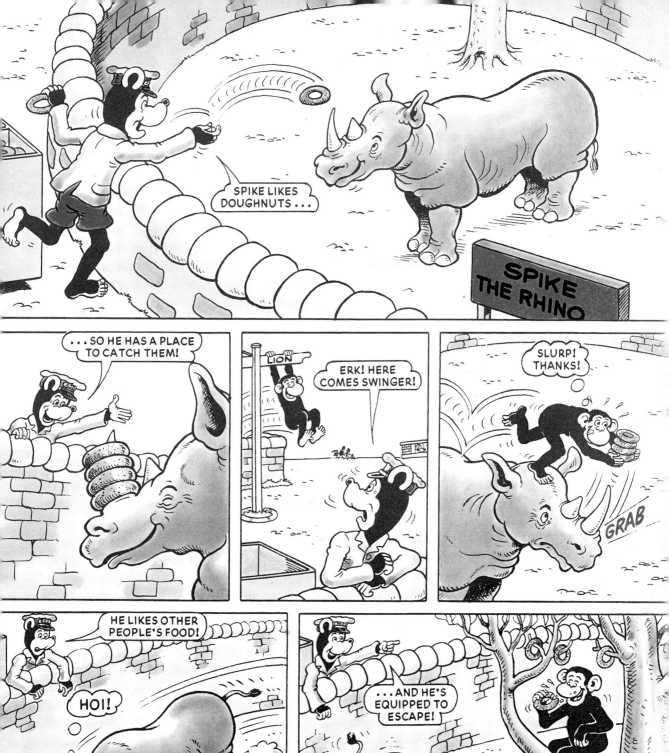

What's that—under his hat?